The Boys fro...

'Ninety-four men must die in th... ...
Mengele. 'We have given years ... . to this work. If you do
what you are asked we shall succeed. The Aryan people will be the
rulers of the world.'

It is 1974, many years after World War II. But in South
America, there are Nazis who escaped from Europe. For
them, the war is not over. One of them is Dr Joseph Mengele.
In Europe, he did terrible things – and he has never stopped.
He has a plan. If it works, the Nazis will be back – stronger
and more terrible than ever.

Yakov Liebermann has caught many war criminals. If
anyone understands the Nazis, he does. But can he find out
what Mengele's plan is? Can he stop him?

If he doesn't, the world will be a different place for Yakov,
and for everyone . . .

Ira Levin was born in 1929 in New York and is one of
America's most successful mystery writers. He became famous
when he was twenty-four with his first book, *A Kiss Before
Dying*.

After this, he took twelve years away from writing books,
and wrote plays and TV films. But then in 1967 his frighten-
ing story *Rosemary's Baby* became one of his most successful
books. By 1978, it had sold five million paperback copies in
the United States alone. Like many of his stories, it was made
into a film, in 1968, with Mia Farrow. *The Boys from Brazil*
was filmed in 1978, with Gregory Peck as Mengele and
Laurence Olivier as Liebermann. After another break from
writing books, Levin wrote *Sliver* in 1991. This became
another popular film, with Sharon Stone.

For a complete list of the titles available in the Penguin Readers series please write to the following address for a catalogue: Penguin ELT Marketing Department, Penguin Books Ltd, 27 Wrights Lane, London W8 5TZ.

The Boys from Brazil

IRA LEVIN

Level 4

Retold by Cherry Gilchrist
Series Editor: Derek Strange

PENGUIN BOOKS

PENGUIN BOOKS

Published by the Penguin Group
Penguin Books Ltd, 27 Wrights Lane, London W8 5TZ, England
Penguin Books USA Inc., 375 Hudson Street, New York, New York 10014, USA
Penguin Books Australia Ltd, Ringwood, Victoria, Australia
Penguin Books Canada Ltd, 10 Alcorn Avenue, Toronto, Ontario, Canada M4V 3B2
Penguin Books (NZ) Ltd, 1982–190 Wairau Road, Auckland 10, New Zealand

Penguin Books Ltd, Registered Offices: Harmondsworth, Middlesex, England

The Boys from Brazil first published in Great Britain by Michael Joseph 1976
Published in Signet 1992
This adaptation published by Penguin Books 1995
10 9 8 7 6 5

Illustrations by Chris Chaisty

Printed in England by Clays Ltd, St Ives plc
Set in 11/14 pt Lasercomp Bembo by
Datix International Limited, Bungay, Suffolk

To the teacher:

In addition to all the language forms of Levels One to Three, which are used again at this level of the series, the main verb forms and tenses used at Level Four are:

- present perfect continuous verbs, past perfect verbs, *was/ were going to*, passive verbs (simple aspects only and with available modal verbs), conditional clauses (using the 'second' or 'improbable' or 'hypothetical future' conditional) and further phrasal verbs
- modal verbs: *have* and *ought to* (to give advice or expressing desirability), *used to* (to describe past habits, states and routines), *must* and *can't* (to express (deduced) likelihood), *may* and *might* (to express possibility or uncertainty), *could* (to express hypothetical ability), *would* (to express willingness) and *had better* (to give advice).

Specific attention is paid to vocabulary development in the Vocabulary Work exercises at the end of the book. These exercises are aimed at training students to enlarge their vocabulary systematically through intelligent reading and effective use of a dictionary.

To the student:

Dictionary Words:

- As you read this book, you will find that some words are in darker black ink than the others on the page. Look them up in your dictionary, if you do not already know them, or try to guess the meaning of the words first, and then look them up later, to check.

CHAPTER ONE

Three men walked into Sadkai's Japanese restaurant. It was early in September, 1974; the city was São Paulo, in South America. Two of them were dressed in dark suits; one had fair hair and one had black hair. They were big men and they looked unfriendly. The third man was dressed in white. He was thinner and older than the others. He smiled and seemed pleased to be in the restaurant.

'My name is Aspiazu,' he said to the young Japanese manager. He spoke in Portuguese, but his accent was German. 'I have booked a private room for this evening.' He was about sixty-three or -four and his grey hair was cut short, with a tidy, matching moustache. His eyes were brown and alive.

'Good evening, Mr Aspiazu,' the manager replied. 'We are ready for you. Please come upstairs. The first door on the right – please take off your shoes as you enter.'

The room was cool, green and sweet-smelling. The door was made of heavy wood, and there was a low black table with white plates and cups on it.

'This is our best room, Mr Aspiazu,' continued the Japanese manager. 'Very nice.'

'I'm sure it is.'

'And we shall bring you dinner for seven people, just like you ordered. Our prettiest girls will serve you!'

But the man in white was looking at the wall opposite. There was another door in it.

'What's behind there?'

'Another private room, sir.'

'Will anyone use it tonight?'

1

'It is not booked, but it is possible that someone will ask for it.'

'I am booking it now.'

The manager was uncertain. 'It is a room for six people. Sometimes eight.'

'Of course,' the man in white replied. 'I'll pay for eight more dinners. My guests will arrive at eight o'clock. One of my men will meet them downstairs. And after dinner we'll have a meeting. We shall talk for some time.'

'You can stay till three in the morning if you like.'

'That will not be necessary. One hour will probably be enough.'

When the manager had left, the man in white sat down and began to read a British **medical** magazine with interest. A waitress brought him a drink.

'What is your name?' he asked her.

'Tsuruko, sir.' She had a flat face.

'She's pretty? Then what are the ugly ones like?' he asked the fair-haired man in German. 'Thank you for the drink, Tsuruko. Now please leave us alone until eight o'clock.'

'Yes, sir.'

The other two men were busy. When Tsuruko left they began to check the room. They looked at the chairs, the walls and the doors. They looked underneath the table and even under the carpet. They looked everywhere in the room, until at last they were satisfied.

The guests arrived on time, at eight o'clock. The fair-haired man waited for them downstairs and the black-haired man stood at the entrance to the private room upstairs. He pointed at the floor and the men added their own shoes to those already there. They were six well-dressed businessmen, all in their middle fifties, all with a fair, North European skin.

They introduced themselves to the man in white. 'Ignacio

Carreras, Doctor . . .' 'José de Lima from Rio . . .' 'I am Jorge Ramos from here in Paulo.'

They sat down with some difficulty at the low table, joking with each other. They gave their orders for drinks to another, prettier young waitress. Then they told each other their German names.

'Yes, I know you! Stangl was your chief, and you were at Treblinka?'

'Did you say "Farnbach"? My wife is a Farnbach, from Langen, near Frankfurt.'

The waitresses brought drinks and then food to the table. Now there were three waitresses: Tsuruko with her flat face, Mori, the pretty one, and Yoshiko, who was dressed very simply. The men ate various kinds of Japanese food, drank tea and beer, and talked about world problems and the new American President, Ford. Then they talked about Japanese women. Kleist-Carreras had some wonderfully funny stories to tell about women in Tokyo; he was a thin man with a glass eye. And while they finished the meal the men talked about fishing and cooking. The man in white asked Mori to marry him. She smiled and said she had a husband and two children.

Finally the meal was over and the waitresses left.

'It is time for business now, boys,' said the man in white. 'You know what you must do. And you know that it will be a long job. Now I am going to give you some details.'

The men were silent. The man in white looked down at some papers.

'Ninety-four men must die in the next two and a half years,' he said. 'Sixteen of these men are in West Germany, fourteen in Sweden, thirteen in England, twelve in the United States, ten in Norway, nine in Austria, eight in Holland, six in Denmark and six in Canada: ninety-four in total. The first

'*The Aryan people will be the rulers of the world. This is our true destiny.*'

man must die on or near the sixteenth of October of this year; the last on or near the twenty-third of April 1977.

'Why? I cannot tell you now, but you will know later. But I *can* tell you that this is the final part of our operation. I and the leaders of our **Organization** have given time and money; we have given years of our lives to this work. If you do what you are asked we shall succeed. The Aryan people will be the rulers of the world. This is our true **destiny**.'

The men looked at one another silently. Then they looked at the man in white again.

'You will leave Brazil with new names,' he continued. 'I have all the papers here. And you will have enough money for two and a half years. Plenty of money, in fact – in diamonds' – he smiled – 'which you must carry in the uncomfortable way. But they are quite small and you will easily find buyers for them.

'All the men are sixty-five years old. They are, or were, all **civil servants**. A few may be dead already, but they were all very healthy when they were fifty-two.'

Hessen, a man with silver hair, was surprised. 'They are all sixty-five?' he asked.

'Yes, they will be when they die. We only have addresses for them from 1961 and 1962, but it will be easy to find them now. Most of them are probably at the same address. They're men with families and responsible jobs.'

'Are they from another organization?' asked Hessen.

'They don't know each other and they don't know us,' answered the man in white. 'Now, here are your orders. Schwimmer, you will go to England. I hear that you can pretend to be a very good Englishman!'

'Certainly, my dear man,' replied Schwimmer in the best Oxford English accent.

The man in white smiled. 'You are all travelling salesmen,

5

from Germany. Farnbach, you will travel in Sweden. And you have fourteen customers.'

He passed a piece of paper to Farnbach, who looked doubtful. 'We kill sixty-four civil servants and the Aryan people will find their true destiny?'

'Was that a question, Farnbach?' asked the man in white. 'I hope not. No, I am sure it was not.'

Farnbach pressed his thick lips together and did not reply.

'We will not succeed immediately, not when the last man dies, but later. The killings will make everything possible. Eventually the Aryan people *will* rule the world. But you must obey the organization's orders now.'

He gave the other men their papers: Norway and Denmark for Traunsteiner, Holland and north Germany for Kleist, the United States and Canada for Hessen, and south Germany and Austria for Mundt.

Mundt smiled; it was not a pleasant smile. 'When I go to Austria,' he said, 'I'll kill Yakov Liebermann too.'

Traunsteiner smiled with him, showing his gold-filled teeth.

'Yakov Liebermann,' said the man in white, 'is old, and ill, and has no money. He gives public talks now; he is not looking for us. If you kill him he'll become a hero. That is not what we want.'

All the men had their papers now, with lists of names and places. The man in white looked at them. 'I have given you dates for the killings, but the exact date is not important; even a month earlier or later will be fine. You can choose how you kill your men, but it must look like an accident or, for example, a killing by thieves, and never a planned murder.'

'Can we pay someone to help us?' asked Kleist.

'You are all sensible men; I'll let you decide. But – one important thing – do not use the men's families in any way.

No meetings with younger wives, nothing like that. Any helpers must be outsiders.' The man in white picked up a pile of thick brown envelopes and gave one to each man. 'Don't open them now,' he said. 'I checked them all myself, this morning. Papers, passports, tickets, visas – everything that you need. And some money for the country that you're going to. You will be given the diamonds tomorrow, on the way to the airport. You will all leave tomorrow.'

'How do we contact you?' asked Hessen.

'Phone your Organization contact in Brazil on the first day of each month,' said the man in white. 'Make it a business call: someone may be listening, you can never be sure. And take no guns, because they search everybody at the airport.

'Any more questions? No? Then we'll have another drink and I shall wish you all good luck.'

◆

'Are you there?' Tsuruko called into the darkness. 'Mr Hunter?'

She stood outside the kitchen door of the restaurant. A man appeared, a tall, young man with brown hair; he was wearing jeans and carried a bag over his shoulder.

'Did you do it?' he asked. He spoke Portuguese with an American accent.

She held up the big rice-bowl and took off the cover. There, inside, was a little cassette **recorder**.

'I put it under the table where they were eating,' she said. 'They didn't see it.'

'Good, very good,' said the young man. 'You are a great help to me!' He put the recorder into his bag. 'This man is a famous film-maker, but he never gives interviews. My magazine will be *very* happy to have this.'

'A North American magazine?'

'Yes. I work for a film magazine, the most important one in the United States.' He smiled brightly at Tsuruko, took out some money and gave it to her. 'Now I am going back to my hotel to eat. Standing outside a kitchen makes you hungry!'

♦

The Germans did not leave the restaurant immediately. They came downstairs to the bar, had more drinks and played some new TV games there. When they fetched their hats, the check-out girl said to Hessen, 'A friend of yours came in after you.'

Hessen looked at her. He was a grey-haired man with a proud face. 'A friend?' he asked.

'Yes – a young North American. I told him you were with a private party and he decided not to go up uninvited. He said it was probably a business meeting, and he was only dressed in jeans.'

'Of course. I know the man; we are all good friends. I am sorry that he didn't come up and say hello.'

Hessen spoke to the man in white. The other men, ready to leave, listened too.

A few minutes later the manager brought the three wait-resses, Tsuruko, Mori and Yoshiko, to the man in white. They looked confused and worried.

The man in white put on a friendly smile. 'Girls,' he said, 'a really bad thing has happened. Bad for me, not for you. You see, I make farm machines; my company is one of the biggest in South America. The men with me tonight are my salesmen. We were talking about some new machines; I gave them all the details. I'm sure you understand that this is a great secret. Now, I have just found out that a spy for *another North American company* was here tonight. My guess is that he

8

A few minutes later the manager brought the three waitresses, Tsuruko, Mori and Yoshiko, to the man in white. They looked confused and worried.

asked one of you in the kitchen to help him. He probably asked you to listen to our conversation.'

Tsuruko, Mori and Yoshiko looked at him and shook their heads slowly.

The manager stepped forward angrily. 'If any of you did this –'

'No, please!' the man in white continued. He smiled at the girls again. 'I'm sure he told you that it was just a joke. He offered you some money? And I know how expensive everything is; how could you refuse? Because I understand all this, I am not angry with you. I just want to know what happened. And I will give you twice as much money as that man gave you.'

Mori and Yoshiko shook their heads again, but Tsuruko was looking down at the money in his hands. Then she looked up at his face, and nodded.

◆

'We must check the hotels,' said the man in white to the waiting men. 'She told us enough about him; we should be able to find him. I'd like to kill her! Hessen will give each of you the names of hotels to go to. The man said that his name was Hunter, but that's probably not his real name. I guess that he is working alone and has arrived recently. A boy – pretending to be a hero, chasing Nazis, pretending to be Yakov Liebermann! We'll catch him easily!'

◆

The young man listened for five minutes, then stopped the cassette recorder and started again from the beginning. God! He listened to the end, to 'the business', as they called it. Then he walked round the room and wondered what he ought to do.

He finally decided that he had to ring up Yakov Liebermann in Vienna. Please be at home, Mr Liebermann! It took a long time for the operator to make the call, and while he was waiting there was a knock at the door.

A waiter came in with a chicken sandwich and a bottle of beer. 'I'm sorry it's taken so long. They all leave at eleven. I had to make it myself.'

God, he was hungry! But when he took a bite from the sandwich he couldn't swallow it.

The phone rang; it was his call from Vienna.

'Mr Liebermann?'

'Yes?'

'Do you remember me – Barry Koehler? I came to see you early in August and wanted to work for you. Barry Koehler, from Evanston, Illinois?'

The phone was silent.

'Mr Liebermann?'

'Barry Koehler, I don't know what time it is in Illinois, but here in Vienna it is too dark to see the clock!'

'I'm not in Illinois, I'm in São Paulo, Brazil. Something's happened.'

'Don't tell me, I'll guess: you saw Martin Bormann. In a bus station.'

'No, not Bormann – Mengele. And I didn't see him, but I've got a cassette recording of him. He was talking in a restaurant.'

The phone was silent again.

'Dr Mengele?' Barry reminded him. 'The chief doctor in the Auschwitz **concentration camp★**.'

'I am not likely to forget Mengele. He ran away to South America because of me.'

★A concentration camp was a Nazi prison; millions of Jewish people were sent there and many were murdered.

11

'I'm sorry – you were so quiet, I had to say something. You must believe me. It *was* him – and other Nazi leaders with him. He's ordered them to kill ninety-four civil servants in different countries, each of them sixty-five years old.'

'Barry, why are you in South America?'

'You wouldn't let me work with you, so I decided to come here by myself. I knew that Stangl works at the Volkswagen car factory, so I waited there. Then I saw a man who looked like Hessen and I began to follow him. And tonight he went to a private party in a Japanese restaurant. A waitress hid a cassette recorder under the table for me. Mengele was talking about the true destiny of the Aryan people and leading the world. I want to play you the recording.'

'Barry, who is going to kill these ninety-four men?'

'Six men from their Nazi organization: Hessen, Traun-steiner, Kleist, Mundt, Schwimmer and Farnbach. You know the names?'

'Not Schwimmer and Farnbach, or Mundt.'

'They have to kill these men on the dates that Mengele gave them.'

'You speak German?'

'Of course! I don't speak it perfectly, but I understand everything. My grandmother *only* speaks German.' He told Liebermann all the other details of the operation.

There was a loud knock at the door.

'Go away!' shouted Barry.

The knocking did not stop. He put the phone down on the bed and went to the door.

'Who's there?'

It was a man's voice. 'There's a Japanese lady who wants to see you, sir. She has an urgent message for you.'

He began to open the door and two men crashed through it. The black-haired Nazi held Barry while the fair-haired

Barry began to open the door and two men crashed through it.

Nazi **attacked** him with a long, sharp knife, until there was blood all over his white shirt. The man in white had come into the room behind them.

'Barry?' the phone asked. 'Are you there?'

The man in white took the cassette out of the recording-machine and put it into his pocket. Then he slowly picked up the phone. He listened, opened his mouth, but did not speak. He put the phone down, cutting off the call. 'I almost spoke to him. I wanted to so much.'

The man with fair hair, who was cleaning the blood from his knife with a towel, looked at him questioningly.

'The Jew and I have hated each other for so long. How much did he hear? It doesn't matter. The men will leave tomorrow. We shall succeed. The world will be ours. It is our destiny. Goodbye, Liebermann. I'll see you at the door of death, in another Auschwitz . . . God will help us.'

CHAPTER TWO

A man sat in a park in Vienna, eating sandwiches. It was Monday, 14 October, and not too cold to have lunch out-doors. He was Sydney Beynon, a journalist from Reuters' news office. He drank some white wine from a paper cup, looked up and saw Yakov Liebermann in front of him.

'Hello, Yakov! It's good to see you.'

Liebermann had already phoned Beynon's office and said that he was coming. Beynon noticed sadly that Liebermann looked old and tired. His wife had died and Liebermann himself had been in hospital. And he had lost all his money when a bank failed – all the money that he had used for his work as an **investigator** of Nazi war crimes.

'How are you, Yakov?'

'I'm all right. In and out of hospital, you know. No – no wine for me, thank you. The doctors won't let me . . . I had a phone call a few weeks ago, in the middle of the night. An American boy rang up from São Paulo; he had a cassette recording of Mengele. You know who Mengele is?'

'One of the Nazis that you want to catch. Right?'

'A Nazi that everyone wants to catch. They called him the Doctor of Death in the concentration camp. He did thousands of medical **experiments** on children, on twins. He tried to make them into good Aryans, tried to turn brown eyes into blue ones. And he killed them all. It's in my book.'

Beynon ate his egg sandwich while Liebermann told him that Mengele was hiding in South America with his own small army of men. He had escaped from his enemies, and the law could not bring him back to Germany.

Liebermann described the plan that the American boy had discovered. 'It might be a joke, but I must investigate it. After the knock at the door there was a lot of noise. Then I heard someone take the cassette out of the recorder and pick up the phone. I am certain that it was Mengele. That person hated me, I could feel it.'

Beynon did not really believe all this. 'What did you do?' he asked.

'I wrote down what the Koehler boy had told me. Later I found out that he had disappeared from his hotel on the same night. That was three weeks ago, and the police won't help. And the first murder is planned for the sixteenth of October. Will you help me, Sydney? It could be another terrible kind of Nazi experiment.'

'What can I do?'

'You can ask your office to send you reports from the newspapers about the deaths of men who are sixty-four to sixty-six years old. In Germany, England, Scandinavia and the United States. And probably France and Holland too.'

'Do you know how many men of that age die every day?'

'A lot, I know, but not in murders, or in accidents that might be murders.' He decided not to tell Beynon that they were all civil servants too.

'All right, I'll try. Shall I send the reports to you?'

'Yes. Start on Wednesday. If the boy is right, there will be several deaths quite soon.'

♦

Emil Döring, sixty-five, lived in the town of Gladbeck, Germany. He no longer worked in his job as a civil servant, but he took regular exercise; he liked to stay healthy. And he had to stay awake, too: he had enemies. There had always been people against him, but this time it was worse: his second wife, Klara, had a lover. Klara was twenty-three years younger than him and her lover was even younger. He was half Jewish and Döring knew that he would like to marry a rich woman. But Emil Döring wasn't ready to die! He was still strong and his old gun was fine too.

He had told Reichmeider, the medical salesman, about all this. He had met Reichmeider here in the Lorelei Bar last night, and they had agreed to meet here tonight too. Reich-meider was a very pleasant man; he laughed at Döring's jokes and was interested in his stories. After a few beers Döring had told him about Klara and her lover. Reichmeider did not believe that Döring was sixty-five! 'No, surely not — you must be about fifty-seven!' What a nice man!

Reichmeider was late. When he arrived he looked very strange, and rather dusty.

'Come outside, quickly! I must talk to you.'

When they were outside he spoke urgently, holding

16

Reichmeider was late. When he arrived he looked very strange,
and rather dusty, 'Come outside, quickly! I must talk to you.'

Döring's shoulder. 'Something's going to happen! Listen, I went into that old, empty building down the road, the one on the corner that they are pulling down. I needed to go to the toilet and I couldn't wait . . . Then I heard that man, Springer, outside on the street –'

Springer! His wife's lover! He had told Reichmeider the man's name last night.

'There were two of them, you see, and one called the other Springer, that's how I knew. They were talking about you. They are planning to attack you, hurt you! They're going to wait for you in the same place. Is that the way you usually go home?'

Döring was so angry that he could only just speak. 'Sometimes,' he whispered.

'Well, that's where they'll be. Two men with sticks, and hats pulled down over their eyes. They don't know that I was there; I found another way out through the house and came out around the corner. You must choose another route home. Unless, of course, you would like to get rid of Springer . . .'

Döring looked at him questioningly.

Reichmeider had thought of a plan. 'This is what you could do. Walk down the street and let them attack you. Then shoot Springer with your gun.'

Reichmeider looked at Döring's coat and smiled. Döring had already told him about the old gun that he carried.

'I'll be there, behind you,' he continued. 'I'll be a witness, and if there is real trouble I'll help you fight them off. It'll give your wife something to think about.'

'Oh, yes!' Döring agreed excitedly. 'Oh, yes, it certainly will!'

Reichmeider told Döring to wait in the empty house while he checked the street. He wanted to make sure that there were only two men, not ten. 'Then I'll come and tell you.

You go out on to the street and walk round the corner. They'll think that you're coming from the bar.'

Döring waited in the old building. Reichmeider was a real friend. He would ask him to dinner tomorrow, and give him a present too. He touched the gun in his pocket confidently. You'll be sorry, Klara.

Now it was Döring who needed to go to the toilet. He had drunk too much beer. As he was opening his trousers he heard a sound above him; somebody was up there. Then there was a noise like thunder. Surprised, hurting, Döring died.

♦

Liebermann was working in the office that was also his dining-room. An envelope from Reuters had arrived, full of reports. 'Man killed in car crash'; 'Robbers murder school-teacher.' So many of them – so many men had died, all about sixty-five years old.

He called Esther, his secretary and helper. 'I need some dictionaries. Swedish, Dutch, Danish and Norwegian. Maybe French too.'

Esther looked at the pile of papers on the table. 'How will you know which ones the Nazis killed?'

'I won't know. Some I can forget about, but I'll have to go and investigate the others myself.' He picked up a German report: a night-watchman, August Mohr, had died in a fire at the factory where he worked. He put it on the pile of unlikely reports, then changed his mind; a civil servant might have a second job at night.

'Do you want something to eat?' Esther asked him.

He shook his head.

'And this is all because a boy rings you up and then disappears.' She shook her head too.

A few hours later he had read all the reports. There were eleven possible ones. Three of these men had died on 16 October: Chambon, Hilaire, in Bordeaux; Döring, Emil, in Gladbeck; and Persson, Lars, in Fagersta, Sweden.

The phone rang and Esther answered it.

There were two on 18 October: Guthrie, Malcolm, in Tucson –

'Yakov? It's a man called Klaus von Palmen, from Mannheim. He rang you once last week, when you were away.'

Liebermann had been away from home, on a **lecture** tour of German universities. The young man said he had heard Liebermann's lecture in Heidelberg, and Liebermann remembered him. He had a clever face and fair hair. He had asked questions.

Liebermann had told the students at the lecture about an 'imaginary' problem, a Nazi plan to kill ninety-four sixty-five-year-old civil servants. Why had they chosen these men? What were they hoping for? The students' suggestions had given him some good ideas for his investigations. Did these men all know one another when they were younger? When they die, who gets their money? Where were they born? Perhaps in the same country? Do they have important relations or friends? And why is Mengele, a doctor, the leader of the operation? Are these murders some kind of an experiment?

Von Palmen had guessed that it was a very real problem and he wanted to offer his help. He had already found out about one of the deaths that was in Liebermann's pile of reports. 'We must check it for ourselves. I'm a law student; I know how to ask questions.'

'And why is this your business? When did "I" become "we"?'

'Are you the only man who can fight the Nazis? You told

us about the problem in public. You didn't say it belonged to you.'

'Listen to me. The person who told me about the problem was a young man like you. He thought that he could help. And now he is probably dead – murdered. Do I want the same thing to happen to you?'

'I can look after myself. Shall I ring you with information? Or shall I keep it to myself?'

Liebermann knew that he could not stop him. 'Do you know what to look for?'

'Of course.'

Liebermann wrote down the young man's address and phone number. Perhaps the boy would be all right; he was certainly clever enough.

'Esther?'

Esther was asleep at her desk, her head on her arms. She woke up. 'Where are you going?'

'To the bathroom.'

'No, no. Where are you going to look?'

'To a place near Essen – Gladbeck. It's all right with you?'

◆

'Not an accident?' The barman at the Lorelei was surprised.

The police had told Liebermann how to find the Lorelei Bar and where Döring's wife lived, but they had no other useful information to give him. They thought that Döring's death was bad luck, not murder.

'Perhaps. I'm trying to find out, for a friend of his. Did he come here often?'

'Once or twice a week.'

'And did he leave alone that night?'

'He was drinking alone, and then he hurried away. He forgot his change – that was unusual.'

21

'He was waiting for someone,' said an old man at the other end of the bar. 'He was looking at the door all the time. Perhaps he was waiting for that medical salesman that he was talking to here the night before he died. Döring talked a lot – he told a lot of stories, and always the same stories.'

'He told them to a salesman?' asked Liebermann.

The old man nodded. 'Yes, a salesman in medicine. The man was laughing. The stories were funny the first time you heard them . . .'

'Do you remember the salesman?' Liebermann asked the barman.

'He had a glass eye. Probably about fifty-five years old. I don't remember any more – it was nearly a month ago.'

Liebermann arranged to see Mrs Döring the next afternoon. He arrived at four o'clock. The door opened and a boy looked out. He was about thirteen, with dark hair, a bony face and a sharp nose. Liebermann wondered whether this was the right flat.

'Does Mrs Döring live here?'

'Mr Liebermann? Please come in. She's on the phone.' The boy took Liebermann's hat.

'Are you her grandson?'

'No.' He was a little annoyed. 'Her son.'

In the sitting-room everything was orange, glass and metal. It looked like a shop, not a home. A woman came in, aged about forty-two or -three. She was small, fair-haired and attractive; she wore a black skirt and jacket and a cream-coloured pullover.

'Please sit down, Mr Liebermann. Would you like some coffee?'

'No, thank you, I had a cup of tea in the café over the road.'

'The Bittner? That's where I work as a hostess, from eight

In the sitting-room everything was orange, glass and metal.
It looked like a shop, not a home. A woman came in, aged about
forty-two or -three.

till three. I'm home when Eric comes back. I only started on Monday, but it seems perfect. Eric, you should go and work on your music!'

'Yes, but I can't answer the door at the same time!' the boy complained, and left the room.

'He's very good,' she said, as he began to play his violin.

'Yes, he is,' said Liebermann.

'He wants to be a violinist when he grows up.'

And Liebermann had wanted to be a pianist, before the war, before the Nazis, before everything. No one ever knows what is going to happen.

He began to question Mrs Döring, but the answers did not help. She did not think that Döring had belonged to any organizations. No one phoned him from abroad, no foreign letters arrived for him. His money was shared equally between his wife, his son and his sister.

'The police told me that he was carrying a gun that night. Why?'

'He always took his gun.'

'*Always?*'

'Always. He was afraid of people.'

'Who was he afraid of?'

'Everyone. He wasn't – he wasn't crazy, but he was a little bit strange. Once I asked him to see a doctor. He nearly shot me! Seriously! He suspected that I was another enemy working against him.'

'Was he a Nazi?'

'I don't know, but he said he wasn't. I didn't meet him until 1952, so I can't be sure. Do you think the Nazis killed him?'

'No, no – I'm just checking possibilities,' said Liebermann.

'Shall I tell you who really killed him?' she asked suddenly.

He looked at her in surprise.

'God. To save me from a very stupid husband, after twenty-two unhappy years. To give Eric a better father, one who will love him and let him play his music. I thank God every night for his death. Doesn't Eric play beautifully? Remember his name; he'll be famous one day.'

It was nearly dark when Liebermann left. The street was busy, full of people and cars. He walked slowly. No, Döring was only important to himself; the Nazis were not interested in him. The salesman was just lonely. Perhaps the search was hopeless. Barry, Barry! Why did you ring me? He began to walk faster.

On the other side of the street Mundt walked faster too.

◆

In Mengele's office, far away in Brazil, a report came in over the radio from Seibert, one of the other Organization leaders. The Organization had sent Mundt to follow Liebermann; someone had told them about Liebermann's lecture and the 'imaginary' Nazi plan to kill ninety-four men. Mengele wanted to kill Liebermann immediately, but the others did not agree. The first seven men were dead on time, with no problems; why make trouble when everything was going so well?

Now Seibert had more news. 'Liebermann went to the house where Döring, our first man, lived . . . He also went to Solingen . . . not our man who died there . . .'

'Then he doesn't understand the plan yet,' replied Mengele. The radio wasn't working well; it was hard for the two men to hear each other.

'He stayed for a long time at Döring's flat.'

'Then we had better kill him at once. Do you agree?' asked Mengele.

'Not while he is in Germany; there will be too much interest in his death.'

The radio wasn't working well; it was hard for the two men to hear each other.

'As soon as he leaves Germany –'

'We'll think about it. I hope you're not planning to go to Europe yourself?' said Seibert.

'How could I go to Europe? You know that's impossible!'

Later, Mengele smoked a cigarette alone in his office. The names of the ninety-four men were painted on the wall. By each name was a little square, which Mengele filled in with red paint as each man died. Was he ready to throw away all his work? To let one Jew spoil his whole life's plan? No, he was not. He looked at the picture on the other wall. There was his leader – his real leader, Adolf Hitler.

'I will not fail you,' he promised.

CHAPTER THREE

'We've only investigated four of the eleven,' Klaus von Palmen said, cutting the thick sausage on his plate. 'We shouldn't stop yet. It's too soon.'

'Am I saying that we're stopping?' Liebermann put his fork into a potato. 'All I said was that I'm not going all the way to Sweden. I may go to other places, and I may ask someone to go to Fagersta for me. Someone who speaks Swedish.'

They were in a restaurant at Frankfurt airport; it was Saturday night, 9 November. Liebermann was on his way back to Vienna and Klaus had driven from Mannheim to meet him. The restaurant was expensive, but Liebermann wanted to give Klaus a good meal. The boy had investigated the death of the man in Pforzheim. No luck there: five people witnessed his death when he jumped off a bridge. He went to Freiburg too, when Liebermann was in Solingen. Mohr, the night-watchman in Solingen, was a civil servant in the day-time, as Liebermann had suspected; but the fire officials had already investigated the accident, and murder was impossible.

In Freiburg, Klaus thought that he had discovered something. The man there, who worked in the Water Department, was killed by robbers near his home. A neighbour had seen someone near the house the night before; she thought that he was watching it.

'A man with a glass eye?'

'She was too far away to see details like that. Why?'

'There was a man with a glass eye in Gladbeck.'

But why would the Nazis want to kill Rausenberger, the man in Freiburg? There was nothing in his life to interest them. And it was the same with all the men: Döring, Müller, Mohr and now Rausenberger. After investigating four of the eleven deaths, Liebermann and Klaus had made no discoveries.

'Look, we'll check out some more men. I'll go to Bordeaux and I'll ask my friend Piwowar in Stockholm to go to Fagersta,' said Liebermann. 'Will that satisfy you?'

'I could go to Fagersta for you. I speak some Swedish,' said Klaus.

'Yes, and that would cost me an air ticket. And you should be at university.'

'That's not a problem. My exam results are going to be very good.'

'What a brain you have! And what makes you so clever?'

'I can tell you something about myself that might surprise you, Mr Liebermann.'

Liebermann listened seriously when Klaus told him that his parents had once been Nazis. Most of the young Germans who wanted to help him were also the children of Nazis. Perhaps there really was a God, working slowly in the world.

◆

When they had investigated thirteen out of seventeen possible murders, with no results, Liebermann decided to forget the whole business. In January 1975 he began a new lecture tour of the United States.

On Thursday, 14 January, he gave a talk in Pittsfield, Massachusetts. Afterwards he signed copies of his book. One woman told him, as he wrote in her copy, that she was from Lenox, not Pittsfield.

'Is that near here?'

'It's only seven miles away. But I would come to hear you speak even if it was seventy!'

16 November: Curry, Jack; Lenox, Massachusetts. Liebermann remembered it from the list. Next morning he borrowed his hostess's car and drove there. It was snowing.

In Lenox he spoke to the chief of police, Degregorio. Degregorio was not sure that Curry's death was an accident. People went out shooting in the forest all the time, but no one had reported the accident, and the bullet had gone straight through the back of his head.

Liebermann visited Mrs Curry, who was not pleased to see him. He drank tea there and felt unhappy when she started to cry. Like Döring's wife she was just over forty, but not so attractive.

'He was such a good man!' she said, as her eyes filled with tears. 'Strong, and patient, and forgiving.'

Liebermann, uncomfortable, looked around the kitchen. He saw old paint, dirty dishes and a box full of empty bottles by the door. There was also a cleverly drawn picture of an aeroplane on the wall.

He asked Mrs Curry the usual questions about organizations and money, but she did not have anything useful to tell him. Then she looked at the door. 'What are *you* doing out of bed?'

The Döring boy stood there. Eric Döring, with dark hair,

29

a sharp nose and a bony face. So Emil Döring and Jack Curry had known each other!

In great excitement Liebermann turned to Mrs Curry and asked, 'What's this boy doing here?'

'He's ill,' she said, 'he should be in bed. This is my son, also called Jack — no, don't come too close with your cold. And this is Mr Liebermann from Vienna. He's a famous man. Jack, what do you want?'

'Just a drink of fruit juice,' the boy replied, in perfect American English. So it was not the same boy.

'Do you know that you have a twin?' asked Liebermann. 'In Gladbeck, in Germany, there's a boy who looks exactly like you. I can't believe it! I thought that it was the same boy, here on a visit.'

'Jack, take your juice and go back to bed,' said Mrs Curry sharply. 'Everyone has a twin like that somewhere. It's not unusual.'

But Liebermann knew that it *was* unusual. Two boys, exactly the same; two mothers about forty years of age; two fathers of sixty-five, both civil servants, both killed last autumn. That could never be chance! But what could it be? Did the boys have the same father? Not very likely. And their mothers were different, so they should not look like twins.

Liebermann thought about all this as he drove back. Twins . . . twins were Mengele's chief interest. His experiments in Auschwitz had all been on twins. So what does that mean?

He asked his hostess, 'May I telephone abroad? I'll pay, of course.'

'Mr Liebermann, please! You are our guest; it's *your* telephone!'

He didn't argue; it was a very big house.

'This is my son, also called Jack — no, don't come too close with your cold.

A few hours later he had spoken to everyone who had helped with the investigations. In at least six of the families there were boys of the same age, who all looked the same and were all good at drawing or music. They had mothers of about forty-two years old and fathers of about sixty-five, who had all died in the last few months.

In the night, in his warm bed, he woke up and realized what the answer must be. Part of the answer, at least.

In the morning he phoned Mrs Curry. 'Mrs Curry, I think your son is **adopted**, but you haven't told him. You were very nervous when I talked about a twin.'

Mrs Curry was silent.

'Who gave him to you?'

'There was nothing wrong with the adoption! We obeyed all the rules!'

'Just tell me the name of the adoption **agency**, please.'

◆

Liebermann flew back to Germany that evening.

'You can't do this!' said Mr Goldwasser, who arranged his American lecture tours. 'We've sold all the tickets. People are coming to hear you!'

'It's life or death, Mr Goldwasser.'

'No one has ever done this to me before. No one will ever book you again in America! Please think!'

'I have thought, and I have to go. I'm sorry.'

◆

The Rush–Gaddis adoption agency had not given Mrs Curry her son, they said. Her husband, at forty-five, was too old for them; they preferred parents in their thirties. But there was one woman who was working at the agency at that time who could have arranged the adoption secretly. He knew her

32

name well: Frieda Maloney – a Nazi concentration camp guard who had escaped to America. Frieda Maloney seemed to be a perfect American – a teacher, and a worker with homeless babies and unwanted dogs. Then two sisters who were once her prisoners at the Ravensbrück concentration camp recognized their old guard in New York and reported her. She was now in prison in Germany.

Frieda Maloney's lawyer agreed to let Liebermann see her for an hour. She seemed quite ordinary, with tired eyes and hair that was going grey. She wore a light blue prison dress and looked like a hard-working waitress. Cruelty, thought Liebermann, is not always obvious in a person. She was willing to talk.

'A man from the Organization asked me to find a job with an adoption agency,' she said. 'It was in 1960. Any job was all right if I could look at the agency's lists. I had to find couples of the right ages: husband born between 1908 and 1912, wife born between 1931 and 1935. The husband should be a civil servant.'

She sent copies of suitable records back to the Organization. Then they told her which families to contact. She spoke to each couple and for a thousand dollars offered them a healthy white baby boy with all the right adoption papers. They had to promise that they would never tell the child about the adoption.

'I fetched each baby from the airport and took it to its new parents,' Frieda Maloney said.

'Where did the babies come from?' Liebermann asked.

'The boys? From Brazil,' Frieda Maloney answered. 'There were about twenty babies in three years.'

'What did they look like?'

'Beautiful,' she said. 'Blue eyes, dark hair. They were all similar. And light skin – they looked European, not Brazilian.'

'Whose babies were they?'

'The boys? From Brazil,' Frieda Maloney answered. 'There were about twenty babies in three years.'

'I don't know. I did it for the Organization, for our Fatherland; I asked no questions.'

'Do you remember their names?'

Frieda Maloney smiled. 'It was thirteen, fourteen years ago,' she said. 'I remember one, Wheelock, because they gave me my dog. The Henry Wheelocks, in New Providence, Pennsylvania. A lovely dog. My husband still has her.'

'Guthrie?'

She nodded. 'Yes – the first family was Guthrie; that's right.'

'He died in October,' Liebermann said. 'In an accident.'

'Between the Guthries and the Wheelocks there was another couple – the Currys,' she said.

She told him the dates of the first three adoptions. They were all close together. If she was right, then they would try to kill Wheelock on about 22nd February, fourteen weeks after Curry.

◆

On Friday 31 January, Mengele was an important guest at the Nazi dance in Hotel Novo Hamburgo, Florianópolis, between São Paulo and Pôrto Alegre. The other guests were excited to see him and told each other how healthy and happy Mengele looked. He was wearing a white dinner-jacket, laughing, repeating new names and kissing cheeks. And yes, he was happy. Tomorrow he could fill in four more little squares on his office wall – eighteen names with red squares in total. They were succeeding! Two months ago he had been afraid that Liebermann would spoil the whole plan. But then the Jew went to the wrong cities, the wrong countries, and finally back home. Liebermann was not a danger to them any more.

Now Mengele was dancing with a beautiful young Nazi woman. His hands moved over her body and he was really enjoying himself when Farnbach danced past him. 'Good evening, Doctor Mengele! How are you? This is my wife, Ilse.'

Farnbach! No, it couldn't be Farnbach! Perhaps he had drunk too much. But when he looked again Farnbach was still there. Mengele stopped dancing.

'You should be in Kristianstad, getting ready to kill Oscarsson.'

His wife, an ugly little woman, opened her mouth in surprise. Farnbach himself turned white.

Mengele jumped on Farnbach, his hands round his throat. The attack pushed Farnbach back against a table; he fell, and the table and all its glasses and plates fell with him. A woman screamed; people turned round to look.

'There's glass in his head!' his ugly wife cried out. 'Oh, my God! Bruno! Get a doctor!'

'This man should be killed! He was given a job to do for the Aryan people! He chose not to do it.'

The guests looked confused. Farnbach was trying to speak, but he could only cough.

Mengele pushed through the men who were standing round Farnbach and looked down at him.

'They called me back!' Farnbach said at last. A drop of blood fell from his ear. 'I *was* in Kristianstad.' Another drop fell. 'They phoned me in Stockholm and told me to come back at once.'

Mengele stared at him. 'Why?' he asked.

'*I don't know*,' Farnbach told him angrily. 'I don't ask questions now. I do as I am told.'

'Where's the *doctor*?' screamed Farnbach's wife.

'I am a doctor,' said Mengele thoughtfully. And to Farnbach he said, 'I'm very sorry,' as he began to take the thin pieces of glass out of his head.

Mengele jumped on Farnbach, his hands round his throat.
The attack pushed Farnbach back against a table.

In the manager's office Mengele phoned Seibert's private number: he was not at home. He rang up the head office of the Organization: no reply. Finally he spoke to Ostreicher, another contact.

'It's Liebermann,' Ostreicher told him. 'He visited Frieda Maloney last week and she probably told him everything. There was a meeting and the bosses decided to bring the men back home.'

'Why didn't they kill Liebermann? Are they mad, or Jews or something? Why?'

'Seibert wanted to kill Liebermann, and so did I. But the others argued that there are seventeen men dead already. That's probably enough for our plan to succeed. If we kill Liebermann people will hear about it.'

'But what if we need more men killed?'

'It wasn't my decision.'

'Thank you. That helps a lot. Good–night,' said Mengele, and rang off.

When Seibert flew to Mengele's home on Monday, there was no one there. In the office there was red paint all over the list of names on the wall, like blood. Seibert and his pilot took out the picture of Hitler, poured petrol over all the papers and put a match to them.

'Will the house burn too?' asked the pilot.

'Yes, but I don't think that the man who lives here will come back,' answered Seibert, as the flames grew higher and higher.

◆

Klaus rang Liebermann: 'I know why the boys look like twins. I know why Mengele and his friends are killing the adoptive fathers on these dates.'

Liebermann was in bed, not well.

Seibert and his pilot took out the picture of Hitler, poured petrol over all the papers and put a match to them.

'It's difficult to explain on the phone,' said Klaus. 'The girl that I live with, Lena, talked about it to a scientist at the university here. Can you come? I'll arrange a meeting with him.'

'What kind of a scientist?'

'A **biologist**.'

A *biologist*? What sort of an explanation could *he* give them?

'I'm going to Washington on the fourth of February — that's Tuesday morning.' Liebermann wanted to talk to the American police before the date on which Mengele's men might try to kill Wheelock.

'Come on Monday, then. We'll meet you at Frankfurt airport and take you back there on Tuesday. You can stay the night with us. We won't waste your time, I promise.'

◆

The biologist, Nürnberger, was a man in his early thirties.

'He put all the children in similar families,' he said, bending back his little finger as he spoke. 'That gives us the answer. He's obviously very clever; the English and the Americans can't do it yet. The Russians may be able to, of course.'

'Excuse me,' Liebermann said, 'but I don't know what you are talking about.'

Nürnberger looked surprised. Patiently, he said, '**Cloning**, of course. Haldane, the English biologist, recognized cloning first. Have you studied any biology?'

'A little,' Liebermann said. 'About forty-five years ago.'

Nürnberger smiled a young man's smile. 'That's when they discovered cloning. I'll try and explain it to you.'

From the long and complicated description that the biologist gave him, Liebermann understood the most important facts. Cloning was a way of **reproducing** a plant, an animal or even a person so that it was exactly the same as the parent. Sex mixes the biology of two parents, but with cloning it was possible to reproduce only one of the parents.

Liebermann said, 'This . . . can be done?'

Nürnberger nodded. 'Scientists have done it, with simpler types of biological life. We don't know about any similar experiments with humans, but of course it's the perfect dream for a nation. Reproduce only your healthiest, cleverest people!'

And Mengele was a doctor, with money, time and a place where he could work on his experiments alone. All he needed was enough young women willing to let the clones grow in their bodies for nine months.

'These boys,' Liebermann said, 'are clones of Mengele?'

'Exact reproductions of Mengele, biologically. But of course they may not be exactly the same in other ways.'

'Excuse me,' said Lena, 'we can eat now.'

She led them to the next room, a kitchen, where bread, salad and red wine waited for them on the table.

'You say that the boys may not be exactly the same as their fathers. What do you mean?' asked Liebermann.

Nürnberger was spreading butter on his bread; Liebermann sat uncomfortably on a small, hard chair.

'Well, if you want to make another Nürnberger, it is not enough just to reproduce me biologically. You must also reproduce my family life: a mother who is always in church, a father who drinks too much and a wonderful uncle who is a teacher. The uncle must die when the boy is nine and the parents must separate two years later.'

Now there was a plate with meat and vegetables in front of Liebermann.

'But we still may not have a new Nürnberger. I listened to the radio, and he will watch television. He will read different

41

books. He may be a different age when he first goes to bed with a girl.' Nürnberger broke up the meat with his fork and continued. 'Mengele knew this. That is why he found homes for so many boys. He will be happy if only one or two grow up like him.'

'Mengele has brown eyes,' said Liebermann. 'These boys have blue eyes.' He sat silently for a moment, then said 'Excuse me' and left the kitchen.

He returned from the next room with a book. His face was white. 'May I ask you a stupid question?'

Nürnberger nodded.

'Must the father of the cloned child be alive?'

'No, not if the scientist has a part of the man's body. A single hair is enough.'

'It's not Mengele,' said Liebermann. He showed them the cover of the book; on it was a picture of Hitler. 'Hitler's father was a civil servant. He was fifty-two when the boy was born. The mother was twenty-nine. The father died at age sixty-five, when the boy was thirteen.'

They left the kitchen and sat down in the next room. No one spoke. Then Liebermann shook his head and said, 'Ninety-four Hitlers. No. No, it's not possible.'

'Of course it isn't,' Nürnberger said. 'They may be very different from Hitler. Most of them *will* be different.'

'But how many will be the same?' asked Klaus.

'I don't know,' said Nürnberger. 'No one knows.'

CHAPTER FOUR

'Mr Kurt Koehler? This is Rita Farb, a friend of Yakov Liebermann's. I understand that you would like to see Mr Liebermann in Washington tonight?'

Liebermann returned from the next room with a book. His face was white. 'May I ask you a stupid question?'

'Yes. My son, Barry Koehler, was killed in South America. They found his body last week – '

'Oh, I'm so sorry!'

'Thank you. There were some notes in his jeans that the Nazis didn't find which Mr Liebermann should see. His secretary told me he was staying in Washington, but I couldn't find him at the hotel there.'

'No, that's right. He changed his plans and stayed with us in New York last night. But he said that he'll be pleased to meet you for dinner.'

'That's wonderful!' answered Mengele. He had waited and searched for Liebermann in Washington for two days. 'What flight is he on?'

'Oh, he's driving, not flying. He's going to Pennsylvania first.'

'Is he going to speak to Mr Henry Wheelock? In New Providence?'

'Yes, that's right. They're going to meet at midday.'

'Thank you so much.'

'Thank *you*, Mr Koehler.'

♦

Wheelock had laughed when Liebermann phoned and warned him about the Nazi plan. 'I used to work in a prison, so I know how to take care of myself. And I have guard dogs here, too.'

'Good. But can they save you from a gun? Let me come and explain everything to you, please.' At least he could warn the man again more fully and then speak to the police.

'All right. Come when you like, I'm always here.'

'Your wife?'

'She teaches. She's out most of the day.'

'And your son? He's at school?'

44

'Yes, when he's not trying to make films. He thinks that he's going to be the next Alfred Hitchcock!'

Films, not art or music, thought Liebermann. But A.H., the right letters.

◆

Mengele hoped to arrive at the Wheelock's house before Liebermann. It was eleven o'clock when he drove along Old Buck Road and saw the sign: 'H. Wheelock. GUARD DOGS.' Dogs – that might be a problem. But he could pretend to be a customer: 'A guard dog – just what I'm looking for.'

As he got out of the car, a tall, white-haired man came round the side of the house. His face was unfriendly. 'You're Liebermann?' he asked.

Mengele smiled. 'Yes!' he said. 'And you're Mr Wheelock?'

A large black dog by Wheelock's side **growled** at Mengele.

'Come in. I want to hear what this is all about.' He held the dog tightly and opened the door. Three more dogs came out, growling. 'Don't worry about the dogs. Boys, this is a friend,' Wheelock said. 'I'm well guarded here, as you can see. So why does someone want to kill me?'

Mengele looked at the photos on the sitting-room wall, all of dogs. There were none of the boy. Wheelock was sitting on the sofa, smoking his pipe.

'Is your son at home?' asked Mengele.

'No one's here except for me and the dogs,' said Wheelock. 'Well? Why is a Nazi coming to kill me?'

Two of the guard dogs pressed their noses against Mengele's legs. Another lay on the carpet between Wheelock and Mengele, and the fourth stood watching his owner.

45

'You know, it's hard for me to talk with these dogs here,' said Mengele, smiling. 'I had a bad accident with a dog when I was eight and I'm still very nervous.'

'You should have told me.' Wheelock jumped up and shut the dogs in the next room.

'Thank you,' said Mengele. 'Now, it's very important that you're safe. I'd like to lend you a gun.'

'I've got one,' said Wheelock.

'But this one is better,' said Mengele, taking it out of his jacket. 'Put your pipe down and your hands up.'

Wheelock stared at him.

'Do it now,' said Mengele. 'I don't want to hurt you. Why should I? It's Liebermann that I'm interested in.'

Slowly Wheelock put his hands on his head. 'But I'm not interested in Jews or Nazis,' he said.

'Good,' Mengele said, pointing the gun at him. 'But I want to put you somewhere where Liebermann can't see you. What's behind that door?' There was another door in the sitting-room, which had a lock on it.

'Stairs that go down to a workroom below.'

'Fine. Turn round, slowly. Now open the door and go down.'

As Wheelock began to walk down the stairs, Mengele shot him – once, twice, three times. Wheelock fell forwards; his head hit the floor below, his legs spread out across the stairs.

Mengele shut the door. 'Quiet!' he shouted at the dogs, who were **barking** behind the other door. Then he went outside and drove his car round to the back of the house where no one could see it.

Liebermann was late. The directions that Rita Farb had given him were not very good. It was twenty minutes past twelve when he arrived. There were about a dozen dogs

'I want to put you somewhere where Liebermann can't see you.
What's behind that door?'

behind a locked gate, all barking loudly. A man with short grey hair and bright brown eyes was waiting for him.

'You're Liebermann?'

'Yes. Mr Wheelock?'

'Come in.'

The house smelt of dogs and those shut inside were still growling.

'It's OK, I shut them up. Some people get nervous when there are dogs around,' said Mengele, smiling.

Wheelock seemed friendlier now than he had been on the phone, but there was something strange in the way that he spoke, a quality in his voice that was not at all friendly. Liebermann couldn't quite understand it. He sat down and began to talk to Wheelock about the adoption agency and the fathers that the Nazis were killing. Wheelock's replies were perfectly natural, except for something in his accent; what was it? And then Liebermann knew. It was not an American voice but a German one. Dear God! He understood. The man's shoes and trousers were for the city, not the country. And the dogs were shut up, growling and barking . . .

'Why are they killing these men?' asked the man who was not Wheelock.

The Nazi killers were men in their fifties and this man was about sixty-five. So who was he? Mengele? Impossible. It would be much too dangerous for him to leave South America.

'So you don't know? Then I must tell you,' said Mengele, bringing out his gun.

Liebermann looked at him again. In his imagination he made his hair longer and darker. He remembered the photos of Mengele as a younger man . . . Yes, Mengele. Mengele! The hated Doctor of Death, the child-killer! He was sitting *here*, smiling, pointing a gun at him.

'Do you recognize me now?'

Liebermann took a deep breath. 'Yes, I recognize you,' he said.

'The other leaders in the Organization are just tired old ladies,' Mengele said. 'They called the men home because you talked to Frieda Maloney, so I must finish the job myself. Sit comfortably, with your hands on your head. You have a minute to listen before I kill you.'

Liebermann thought about the door on his right. If he could just reach out to open it, perhaps the dogs would see Mengele with the gun and attack him.

'This is one of the most satisfying moments of my life,' said Mengele.

'Is Wheelock dead?' asked Liebermann.

'No,' Mengele said. 'He's in the kitchen, making lunch for us. Listen now, dear Liebermann. I've found some photos' – he reached for a book on the table next to him – 'and they are all of *him*. Hitler. He's alive again. The boy who lives here is *him*, and so are all the other ninety-three boys. Exact clones of our leader. Hitler knew about the experiments that I wanted to do; he gave me some of his blood. You thought that my experiments at Auschwitz were useless, but no, they weren't.'

Liebermann stood up and there was a gunshot. He felt pain in his chest, but he reached for the door. It opened.

The dogs barked wildly and ran through. There were more gunshots, barks, and then three big black dogs stood over Mengele on the sofa. His gun was now empty. The fourth dog lay dead on the floor.

Liebermann was on the floor himself, his back against the wall. 'Kill!' he shouted at the dogs. Nothing happened. 'KILL!' he shouted again, but the pain in his chest was terrible and only a whisper came out. The dogs growled and did not move.

'Are you alive, Jew?' said Mengele. Liebermann was dreaming. He opened his eyes. Mengele was sitting up now, but the dogs were still around him. 'Too bad. But I can see that you won't be with us for long. And these dogs will forget about me soon. Water? Drink? Good dogs. Go and have a drink.' The dogs growled. 'So you've failed, Jew-boy. But we will succeed. I shall soon walk out of here, and every man on that list will die at the right time.'

Liebermann did not hear any more until the dogs out the back began to bark again. There was somebody outside. It was the boy.

He stood at the door of the sitting-room, another dark-haired, sharp-nosed boy. He looked at Liebermann. He looked at Mengele and the dogs. He looked at the dead dog, his blue eyes wide. 'Hell!' he said.

'My dear, dear boy,' said Mengele, looking at him lovingly. 'I am so happy to see you! Please take these dogs away. They have kept me here for *hours*. They thought that I wanted to hurt you, but it was that Jew over there who came here to do you harm.'

The boy stared at him and turned his head slowly towards Liebermann. Liebermann shook his head.

'Where's my father?' the boy asked Mengele.

'I don't know,' Mengele answered. 'Perhaps this man has killed him. I came to visit your father and found the Jew here with a gun. I was able to take the gun away from him, but then he opened the door and let the dogs in. Call off the dogs and then we can look for your father.'

'Chocolate!' said the boy. The dogs turned away from Mengele and ran up to him. He touched their heads.

'Chocolate!' said Mengele happily. 'I couldn't have guessed that word!'

'We had better call the police,' said the boy.

50

Mengele stared at him. 'How wonderful you are!' he said. 'Yes, we must certainly call the police. But could you take the dogs into the kitchen and fetch me a glass of water and something to eat?' He stood up. 'I'll phone the police, and then I'll look for your father.'

'Is that your car out at the front of the house?' the boy asked.

'Yes,' said Mengele.

'It has a sticker from a Jewish club. You called *him* a Jew.'

'Don't worry about that,' said Mengele. 'Bobby dear – '

'Toast,' said the boy, and the dogs ran growling at Mengele. He sat down again on the sofa.

'Chocolate! Chocolate!' shouted Mengele.

'They won't listen to *you*,' said the boy. He looked at Liebermann. 'He changed the story. *He* had the gun and let *you* in. Isn't that right?'

Liebermann nodded.

'Can't you talk?'

He shook his head and pointed at the phone.

'That man is your enemy!' cried Mengele. 'I'm your friend, Bobby. I'm the doctor who was there when you were born. I know all about you. I know that you're really clever – more clever than the teachers at school. And that you want to be a great artist.'

'No, I want to make films.'

'Yes, of course,' said Mengele. 'You want to be a great film-maker. You argue about this with your father. He's old and doesn't understand. It makes you angry.'

The boy looked at him.

'You see,' Mengele said, 'I *do* know you, better than anyone in the whole world. Your parents are not your real parents; they adopted you. I arranged it all.'

The boy stared.

'I know this is sudden. But don't you feel like a prince in a country where nobody understands you?'

The boy stood taller. 'I feel . . . different from everyone sometimes.'

'You *are* different,' Mengele said.

'Who are my real parents?' the boy asked.

Mengele looked thoughtfully at his hands. 'I'll tell you when you are older. But you have the best blood of all. Believe me and I will give my whole life to you.'

'Who are my parents? I want to know.'

'I will tell you at the right time – '

'Tell me *now*. Or I'll make the dogs kill you. I'll count to three. One . . . '

'You have no parents!' Mengele said.

'Two . . . '

'It's true! You are born again from the greatest man who ever lived. And that Jew over there is his enemy, and yours. You are the son of Adolf Hitler! A good man, a great man! And through you he will save the world!'

'You're crazy,' said the boy.

'Do as I tell you. Let me look after you. The highest destiny of all is waiting for you.'

'Sausages,' said the boy.

The dogs jumped at Mengele. He cried out. Liebermann looked, and looked away again. There were wet sounds, growling sounds, tearing sounds.

'Off,' said the boy at last. He came and stood by Liebermann. 'I think you need help fast or you'll die soon.'

Liebermann nodded.

'I could go out and come back later. No one will know that I was here. You'll be dead then. If I phone the police now, are you going to tell them what I did?'

Liebermann thought for a moment, then shook his head.

'You are the son of Adolf Hitler! A good man, a great man!
And through you he will save the world!'

'Promise?'

Liebermann nodded.

'He really was crazy,' said the boy, and went to the phone.

When he came back Liebermann whispered, 'There's a list of names. It may be in his coat pocket.'

He watched the boy go out of the room. My helper, Hitler. He looked at Mengele; there was only bone and blood where his face used to be. Good.

The boy came back with some papers. 'My father's name is here,' he said, and gave them to Liebermann. 'I forgot, I should go and look for him.'

Liebermann closed his eyes. Stay alive. Not finished yet.

There was barking in the distance.

'I found him,' said the boy.

♦

Liebermann lay in hospital. The doctors had told him that he was going to be fine. The police came to see him. They knew that Mengele had come from South America on a false passport and that he *might* be a Nazi, but that was all. 'You had better be more careful in future, sir.'

'I will. Thank you.'

Mrs Wheelock came to see him. Her son was going to be a great success. He had filmed the ambulance, the police and the bodies, and the film was shown on television all over the country.

Mr Goldwasser, the tour manager, rang. Did the flowers arrive? Good, and perhaps he *could* talk about another tour for Liebermann. The public was very interested after all they had read in the newspapers about the killings.

Some other Jewish investigators who had already helped Liebermann came to see him. They knew most of the story already and they wanted to kill the boys.

54

'We can't take any chances. If only one becomes another Hitler, our children will die.'

'*They* are children too,' Liebermann said. 'How can we kill them? We don't *know* that any of them will be new Hitlers. They are his biological clones, but they may be very, very different from him. Leave the boys alone. Excuse me,' he said, 'I must go to the toilet.'

While he was there he tore up the list of names into little pieces and washed it away, for ever.

Rita and Marvin Farb came to take Liebermann out of hospital and back to their home for a rest. Marvin Farb gave Liebermann another piece of paper: the hospital bill.

'Good God!' said Liebermann, when he looked at it.

'This is cheap,' said Farb. 'In New York it could be twice as much.'

♦

The boy was working in his bedroom, making a model of an enormous meeting-room, big enough for thousands of people. It was great, with Dad gone. Just he and Mum. There was no more fighting when he wanted to work on his models. Well, he had loved his father, of course, but it was certainly easier now.

There was a platform in the meeting-room. Who should stand on it? Someone important. Someone who was really good, who people loved. He moved his sharp nose closer to the model and could almost hear the people shouting for their leader. Yes, just like in those old Hitler films.

EXERCISES

Vocabulary Work

Look again at the 'Dictionary Words' in this book.

1 Write a short paragraph about Mengele. Use these words:

experiment	*clone*	*concentration camp*	*adopt*
biology	*agency*	*reproduce*	*medical*

2 Use these words to complete the sentences.

growling *attacked* *civil servant*
barking *cassette recorder*

a The dogs . . . Mengele, . . . and . . . .

b Many radios have a built-in . . . .

c Hitler's father was a . . . .

3 Which word means the same as:

a what is going to happen to you in the future.

b a talk given to a large group of people.

c a group of people all officially working together.

Comprehension

Chapter 1

1 Why do you think 'Mr Aspiazu' booked the extra room in the restaurant?

2 In what ways are the ninety-four men on Mengele's list all similar?

3 Why did the Nazis kill Barry Koehler?

Chapter 2

4 Describe one of the experiments Mengele did on children.

5 What is Eric Döring clever at?

Chapter 3

6 What is unusual about Jack Curry and Eric Döring?

7 What was Frieda Maloney's job fourteen years ago?

8 How old was Hitler when his father died?

Chapter 4

9 What is Bobby Wheelock clever at?

10 How is Liebermann saved from Mengele?

At the end of the whole book.

11 In what ways are the ninety-four men on Mengele's list all similar?

12 Where did Mengele work and what did he do during the war?

13 How did Klaus von Palmen first hear about the Nazi plan?

14 How did Liebermann first try to find the names of the men on Mengele's list?

15 What did Liebermann discover in Lenox, USA?

16 How did Mengele discover where Liebermann was in the United States?

17 The adopted boys were all clever in a similar way. In what way?

18 Who arranged the adoptions of the boys, and how?

19 What was the real purpose of Mengele's experiments with twins and cloning?

20 Why do you think the Wheelock boy finally chose to kill Mengele and save Liebermann?

Discussion

1 What do you think will happen after the end of this story? Will the Döring, Curry or Wheelock boy grow up to be a new Hitler? What could anybody do to stop that from happening? Do you think that Liebermann was right to tear up the list of names and throw it away?

2 Scientists are already able to clone animals and plants. Do you think it would be a good or a bad thing to clone people too? What might be the advantages or disadvantages of cloning?

Writing

EITHER: Liebermann reads about Döring's death in a newspaper report. Write that report (150 words).

OR: The Wheelock boy's film is shown on the television all over the United States. Write the words for the newsreader, to go with the film.

Review

1 In what ways does Mengele change during this story? Give examples to show what you mean.
2 What do you think is the most exciting part of this story? Why?
3 Would you advise your friends to read this book? Why or why not?